S L I D E S
FLIPS AND TURNS

LOUIS R. KRONER

DALE SEYMOUR PUBLICATIONS

Managing Editor: Michael Kane
Project Editor: Joan Gideon
Production Manager: Janet Yearian
Production Coordinator: Leanne Collins
Design Manager: Jeff Kelly
Cover Design: Rachel Gage
Text Design: Detta Penna

Dale Seymour Publications is an imprint of Addison-Wesley's Alternative Publishing Group.

DALE SEYMOUR PUBLICATIONS
P.O. BOX 10888
PALO ALTO, CA 94303

Order Number DS21222
ISBN 0–86651–730–8

4 5 6 7 8 9 10–ML–98 97 96 95

This Book Is Printed
On Recycled Paper

CONTENTS

INTRODUCTION

At first glance, this may seem to be a book of miniature crossword puzzles, lacking only the clues. But look again—it's really a mathematics book. The reproducible activities, intended for grades 3 to 8, are designed to help students

- Understand the geometrical concept of transformation through translation (slides), reflection (flips), and rotation (turns).

- Develop their spatial awareness through visual orientation and analysis of patterns.

- Apply deductive logic to solve problems in visual thinking.

Slides, Flips, and Turns is divided into two parts. Part One, with its activities based on patterns of black-and-white squares in 5-by-5 grids, helps students recognize—and perform—translations, reflections, and rotations. They learn that these motions leave a pattern itself unchanged, but change its position or orientation. Part Two, which involves more elaborate geometric designs, challenges students to apply their knowledge of symmetry to finish shading in the incomplete black-and-white patterns.

Part One

Before doing the activities in Part One, students must understand the meaning of the motions **slide, flip,** and **turn.** The definitions given at the end of the introduction illustrate and explain the three motions, using grid patterns. Make transparencies of these two pages for class discussion, or copy them for each student. Be sure that students become familiar with the following terms, which are used throughout the Part One activities to identify particular motions:

Slide   Flip V   Flip H   Turn 90°   Turn 180°   Turn 270°

Once the students know how to do slides, flips, and turns, they will need to understand the different formats on the activity pages. To introduce these, use Examples A to F (on pages 9–14) either as transparencies or handouts.

The activities are presented in an increasingly complex progression, so you may want to have students work through some of the earlier pages before trying the more difficult types of activities later in the section. In some of the activities, the 5-by-5 grids are separated by a little white space; in others, the grids are connected. Have students work first with the separated patterns, building understanding and confidence, until they are ready to try the more challenging connected patterns. Of course, ability levels vary; some students may want to start with the more challenging activities, while others will work only with those involving the separated grids.

Slides, flips, and turns to shade and to analyze

In the most basic activities, the students look at a given pattern of shaded squares on a 5-by-5 grid, then follow instructions to slide, flip, or turn the pattern in their minds and shade the result on another grid.

Flip V

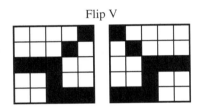

To demonstrate this type of activity, you can use Example A as a transparency, covering the answers until students have worked on the questions, or as a handout.

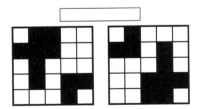

As the next step, students look at a given shaded pattern, along with an adjacent shaded pattern, and analyze the two in order to determine which motion was applied to the original to get that result. They write their answer in the box.

Use Example B to demonstrate and explain this type of activity.

For some of these basic activities, students need to make or follow the changes **horizontally,** in rows across the page. In other cases, they need to make or follow the changes **vertically,** in columns down the page. The description of the motion that changes one shaded grid to the next is printed (or will be written by the students) *over* the two grids for horizontal changes, or *between* the two grids for vertical changes.

You can use Example C to show students how to complete problems that are set up vertically.

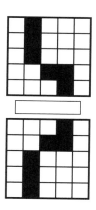

Matching: Finding the result of a motion

Among the more challenging activities in Part One are those that present a 4-by-4 matrix of grids filled with a variety of patterns. In the matrix, rows are labeled with letters and columns with numbers. Just like on a map, any particular grid can be identified by a letter and a number.

The directions identify a particular grid and a motion or motions to be performed. The student's task is to find the resulting grid. Example D will help you introduce this type of matching activity.

Full grid: Making a series of slides, flips, and turns

In the next type of activity, students are given a single grid pattern and must follow directions to fill the entire page with slides, flips, and turns of that one pattern. The motions to be made are described in a separate table (rather than positioned between the grids, as in earlier activities); be sure the students understand how to relate the table to the grids.

Use Example E to show students how to proceed with this type of problem. The students first complete the vertical column at the far left, and then make the horizontal changes across the page for each row.

In a similar, slightly harder activity, students are given an entire series of completed patterns; their challenge is to identify the motions that produced the pattern in each ensuing grid, and write them in the blank table.

	Flip V	Slide	Turn 90°
Flip H	Slide	Turn 90°	Flip V

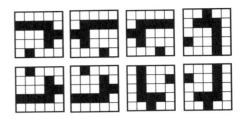

In a number of these activities, students will be asked to identify the **negative image** of the grid after the specified motion; be sure that students understand what this means.

Flip V

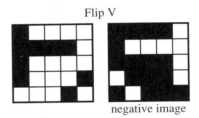

negative image

Diagonal patterns

The last activities in Part One involve more complicated grid patterns made with diagonal lines. The student must add diagonal lines to the blank grids in order to properly shade the slides, flips, and turns. Use Example F to demonstrate this type of problem.

Turn 180°

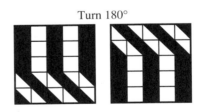

Working in the classroom

For any of the activities in Part One, students can work alone or in pairs. With a cooperative group of four students, each pair could complete one page; then the pairs could trade pages and check each other's work. The answers to Part One are provided in the back of the book for reference when students may disagree about an answer. Students can also design their own problems for others in their group to solve, using the reproducible blank pattern grids on pages 15–17.

Some students may have difficulty visualizing patterns when both flips and turns are called for. To help, let students make a copy of the original grid and shade the pattern on the reverse side by holding it up to a light source (such as a window), or by coloring over the pattern on the front with a marker that will bleed through to the back. Laminate each such grid to make inexpensive, two-sided manipulatives that can actually be flipped over and physically turned to reveal the result of the motions.

Part Two

Part Two of the book continues to work with reflection and rotation as students complete symmetrical designs. In order to do the Part Two activities, students need to understand symmetry. Examples from nature—such as the human body—are a good place to start, although natural examples generally exhibit only *approximate* symmetry. You might use typeset letters of the alphabet, geometric figures, and manufactured objects or designs to demonstrate *exact* symmetry.

There are two kinds of symmetry—bilateral (or reflective) symmetry and rotational symmetry. Most students will be familiar with bilateral symmetry, in which a line drawn through the center of a figure divides it into two halves, each a mirror image of the other. The line that divides the figure in that way is called the line of symmetry. Approximate bilateral symmetry is apparent in natural objects such as butterflies and leaves; it is also found in certain letters of the alphabet, including the uppercase letters A, D, and M.

Other figures have what is called rotational or turn symmetry. Each such figure has a point called its center of rotation. When the figure is turned around that point, it will correspond to itself in something less than a full 360° turn. Approximate rotational symmetry can be seen in nature in such creatures as the starfish. The uppercase letters N, S, and Z have rotational symmetry; their angle of rotation is 180°. An equilateral triangle not only has three lines of symmetry; it also has rotational symmetry around the center, with an angle of rotation of 120°.

You might challenge students to discover which letters of the alphabet have both bilateral symmetry and rotational symmetry.

Part Two contains four types of activities, progressing in difficulty, as follows:

Shading single reflections. In the first type of activity, students are presented with a half-shaded geometric pattern. They imagine a line of symmetry and shade the reflection of the original.

Shading multiple reflections. Slightly more difficult are the activities in which students must make more than one flip to complete the entire pattern.

Shading rotations. For this type of activity, students are given a shaded design along with an identical unshaded design that has been turned. Students work to shade the turned pattern to match the original.

Constructing and shading single reflections. In these, the most difficult activities in Part Two, students must first draw in the lines needed to complete the pattern, and then shade the reflection.

Because all the results for Part Two can be checked visually, the answers are not provided in the book.

Slides (Translations)

The shaded pattern on the first grid simply slides horizontally or vertically into exactly the same position on the new grid.

Slide

Slide

Flips (Reflections)

The shaded pattern on the first grid flips over the imaginary line of symmetry between the grids into the second grid. The result is a mirror image of the original pattern. The flip can be across a row over a vertical line of symmetry (Flip V) or down a column over a horizontal line of symmetry (Flip H).

Flip V

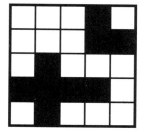 

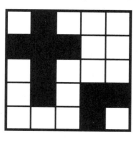

Flip H

Turns (Rotations)

The pattern is rotated in a *counterclockwise* direction. The original grid patterns has been turned 90° or one quarter turn and then shaded on the adjacent grid.

Turn 90°

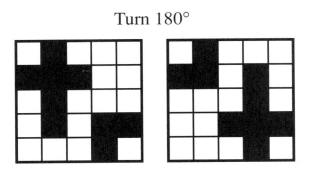

Below on the left the original pattern has been turned 180° or one half turn and then shaded on the next grid. The figure on the right shows the result of turning the original figure three quarters of the way around or 270°.

Turn 180°

Turn 90°

Turn 270°

Slides, Flips, and Turns

Example A

The design in the first grid is changed by the motion written above the first two grids to give the design in the second grid. The grid patterns change across the page.

Shade the grids to show the result of the indicated motions.

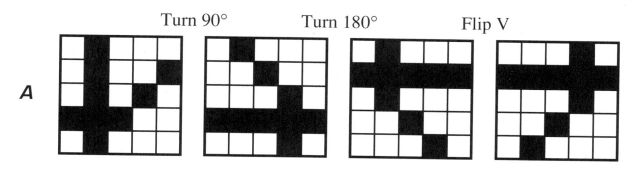

Finish these two examples.

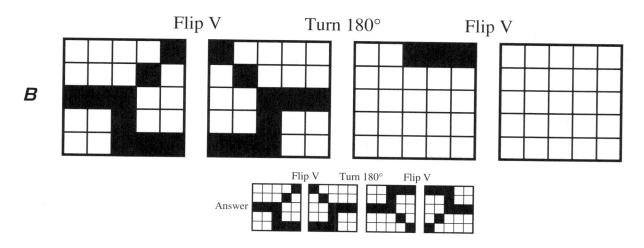

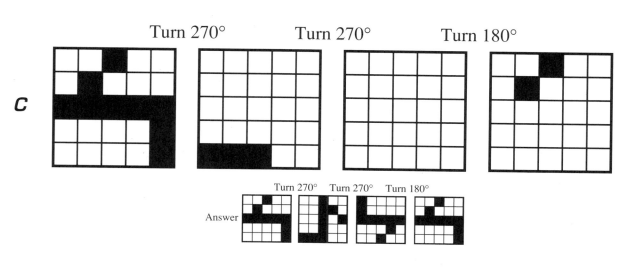

Example B

The design in the first grid is changed by the motion written above the first two grids to give the design in the second grid. The grid patterns change across the page.

Indicate the motion that changed one grid pattern into the next.

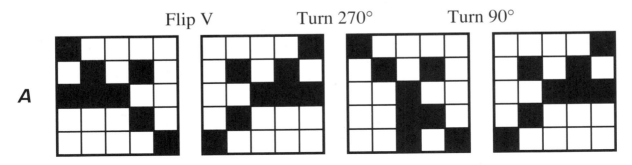

A
Flip V   Turn 270°   Turn 90°

Finish these examples.

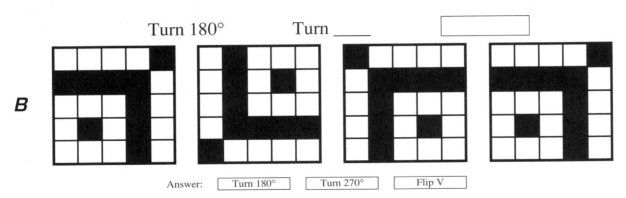

B
Turn 180°   Turn _____   [   ]

Answer: Turn 180°   Turn 270°   Flip V

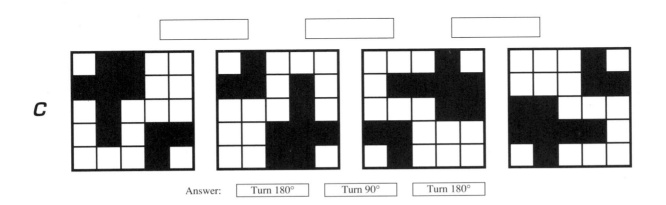

C

Answer: Turn 180°   Turn 90°   Turn 180°

Example C

The design in the first grid is changed by the motion written between the grids into the design in the grid below. The grid patterns change down the page.

Finish these examples.

1

2

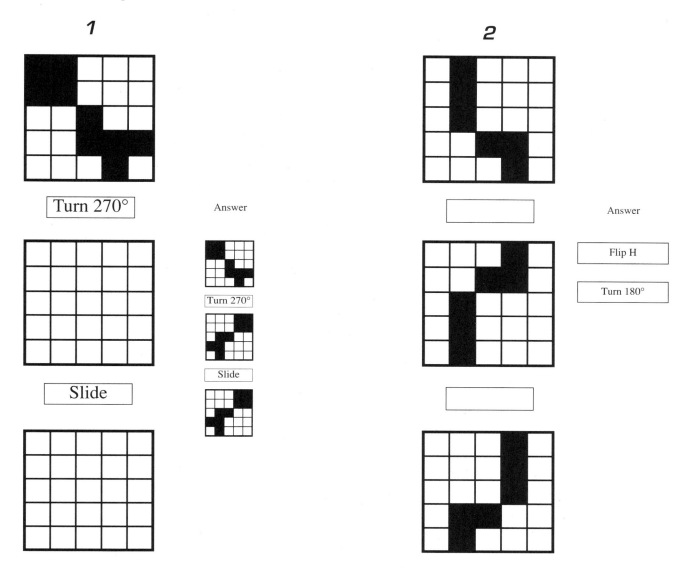

Turn 270°

Answer

Slide

Answer

Flip H

Turn 180°

Example D

To solve these examples, use a coordinate system that divides a space into horizontal rows and vertical columns. The rows are identified by letteres, and the columns are numbered. Use the letters and numbers to pinpoint a particular place on the grid. On this example grid, block A-3 has been marked with an "X" and block C-1 has been marked with an "O".

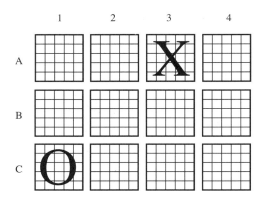

Identify the grid pattern that fits the description given.

Start with Grid	Do the Motion	End with Grid
1. A-1	Turn 270°	_____
2. A-2	Flip V	_____
3. A-3	Turn 270°	_____
4. B-4	Flip H	_____

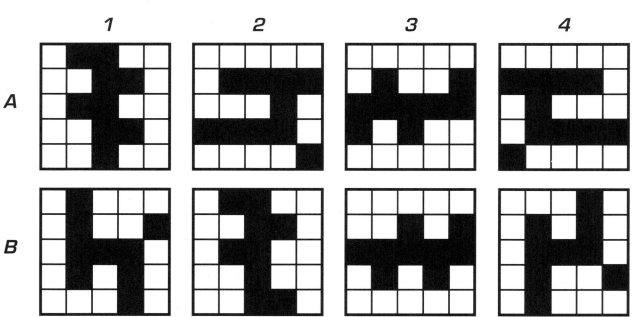

Answers: 1. B-3   2. A-4   3. B-2   4. B-1

Slides, Flips, and Turns

Example E

Only the grid in the upper left-hand corner has been shaded. Follow the directions given in the table to shade in each of the grids. Complete the vertical moves in the first column on the left before completing any horizontal moves.

	Flip V	Slide	Turn 270°
Flip H	Slide	Turn 270°	Flip V

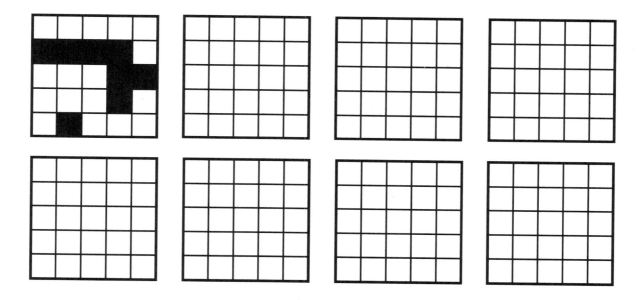

Answer:

	Flip V	Slide	Turn 270°
Flip H	Slide	Turn 270°	Flip V

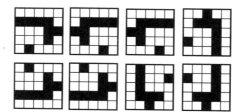

Example F

Add diagonal lines to the blank grids before shading them. Look at the first grid to see what diagonal lines were added. Now slide, flip, or turn those lines to see where they will be on the blank grid. After you have drawn the lines, shade the pattern.

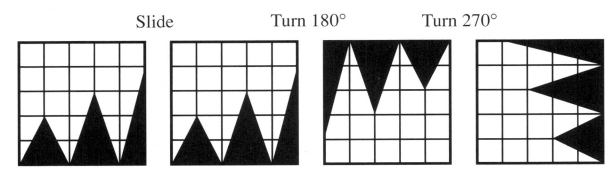

Finish these examples.

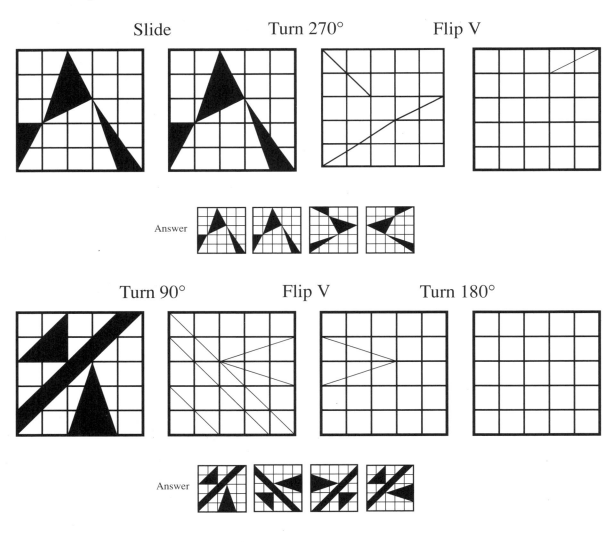

Slides, Flips, and Turns © Dale Seymour Publications

Blank Grids

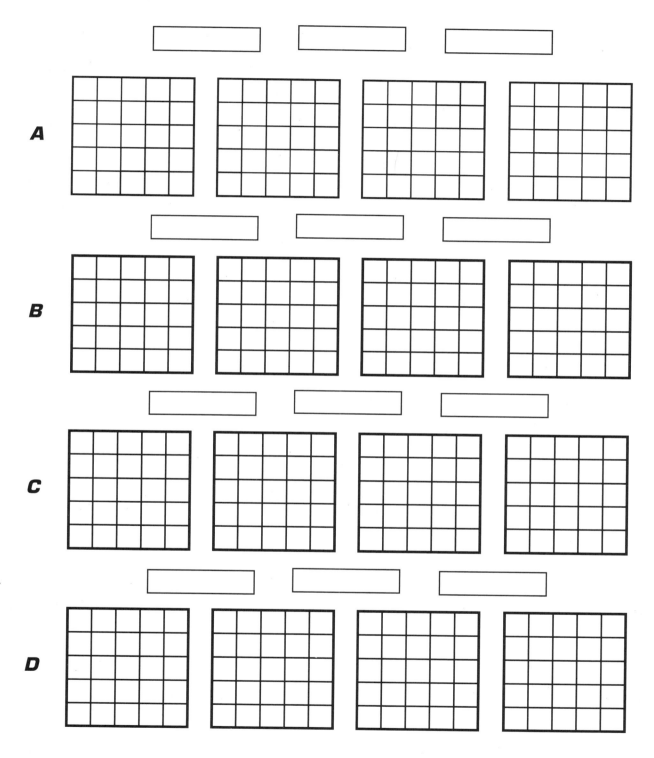

Blank Grids

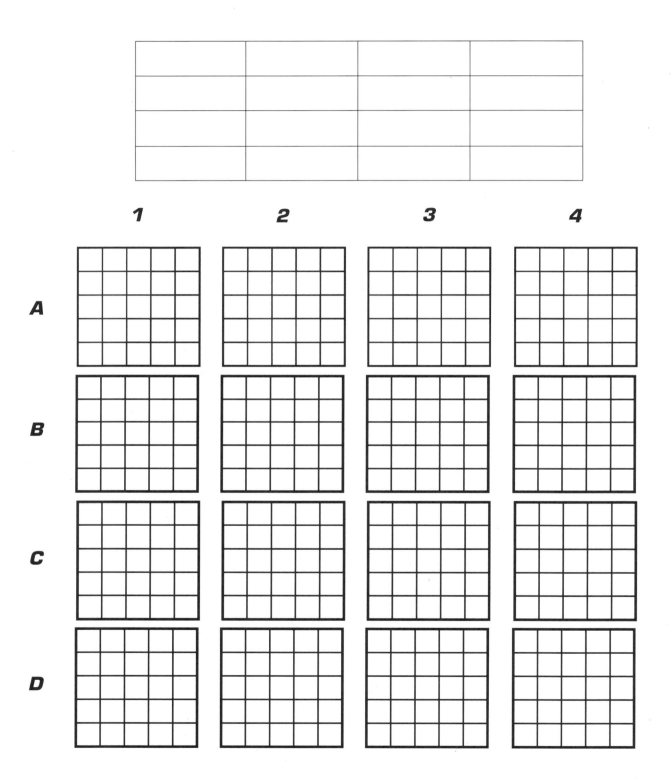

Slides, Flips, and Turns   © Dale Seymour Publications

Blank Grids

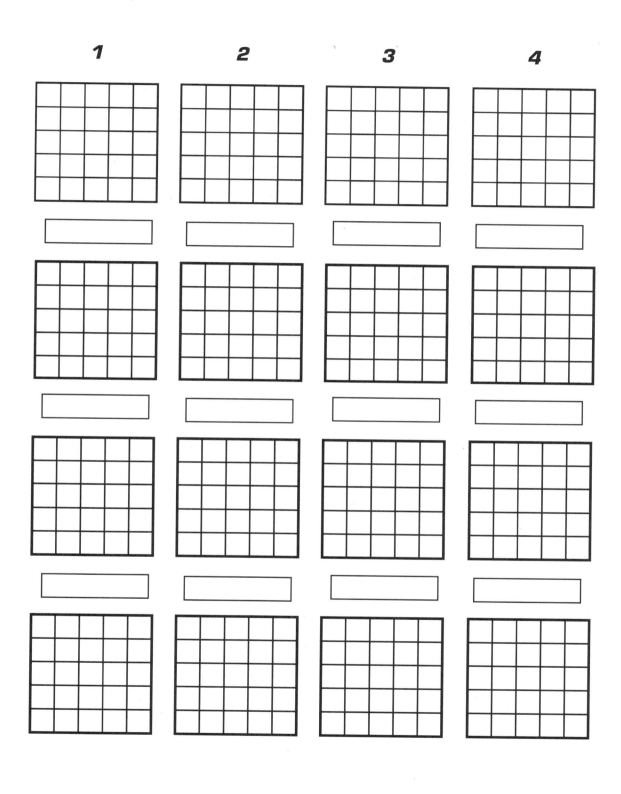

Part One
Grid Patterns

Shading Slides and Flips 1

Shade the grids to show the results of the slides or flips
across the rows.

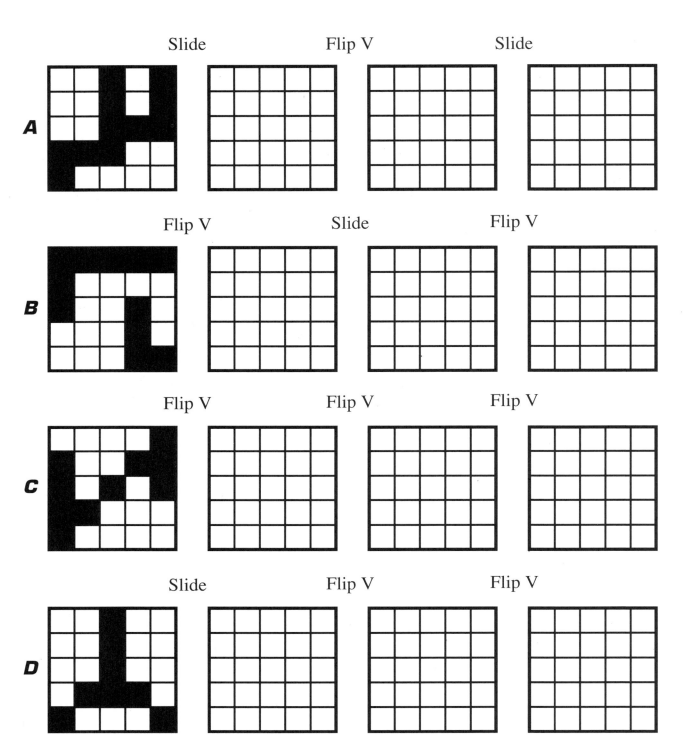

Slides, Flips, and Turns

Shading Slides and Flips 2

Shade the grids to show the results of the slides or flips across the rows.

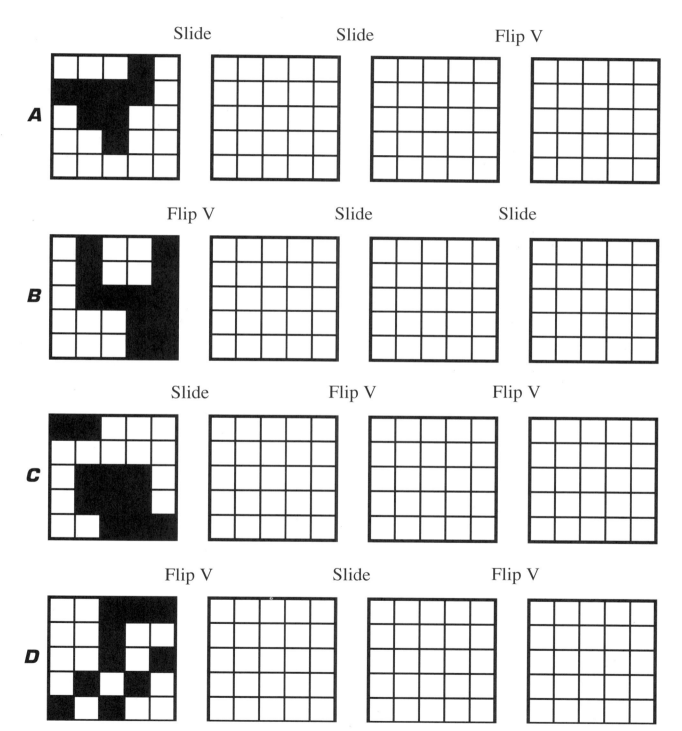

Shading Slides and Flips 3

Shade the grids to show the results of the slides or flips down the columns.

1	2	3	4

Slide	Slide	Flip H	Flip H

Slide	Flip H	Slide	Flip H

Slide	Flip H	Flip H	Slide

© Dale Seymour Publications

Slides, Flips, and Turns

Shading Turns 1

Shade the grids to show the result of the turns across the rows.

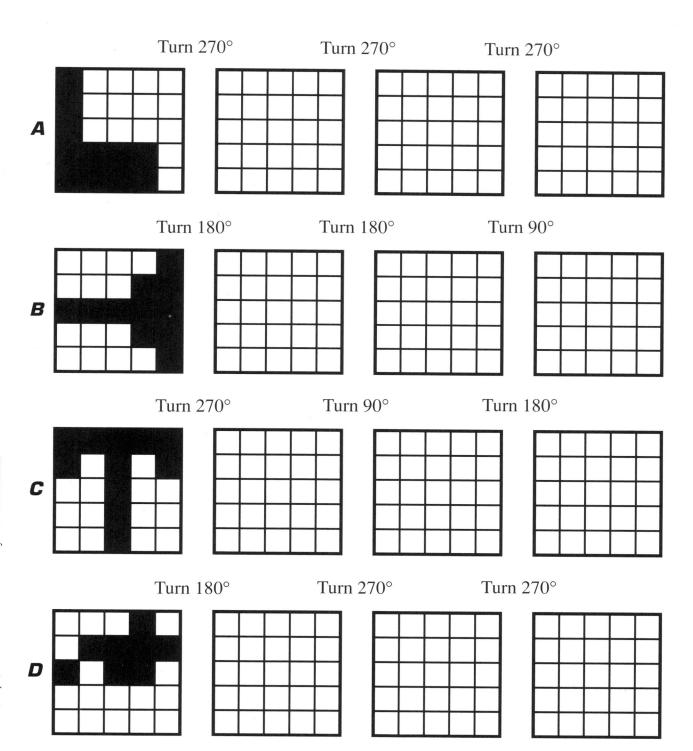

Shading Turns 2

Shade the grids to show the result of the turns across the rows.

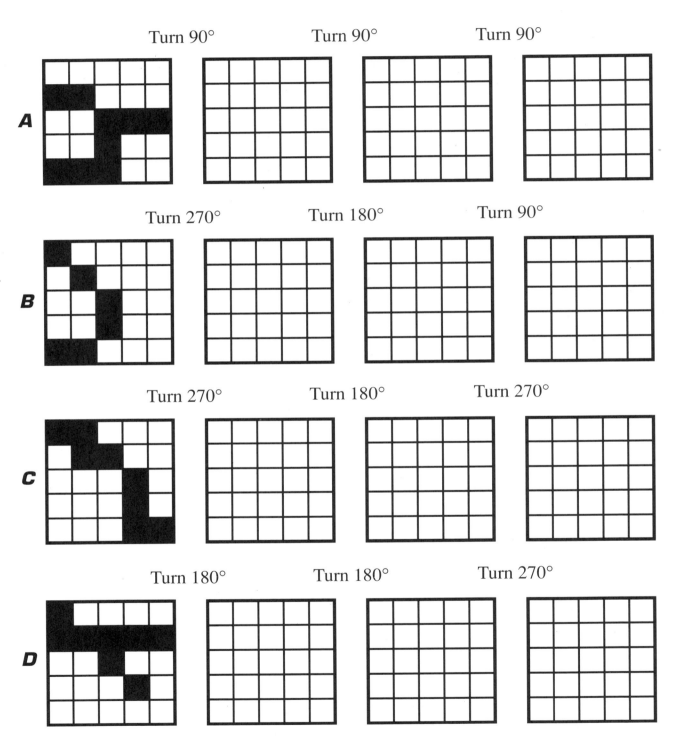

Shading Turns 3

Shade the grids to show the results of the turns down the columns.

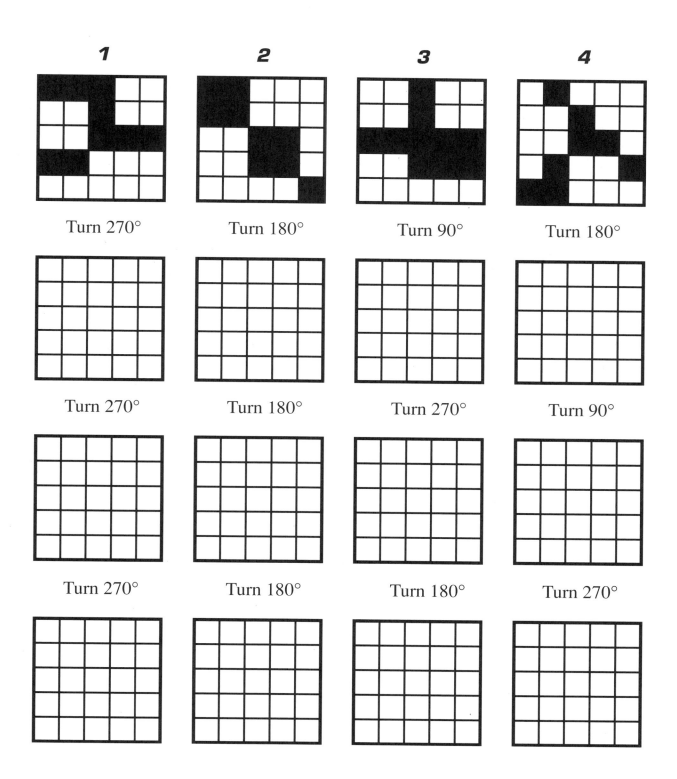

Slides, Flips, and Turns

Shading Combinations 1

Shade the grids to show the results of the slides, flips, and turns across the rows.

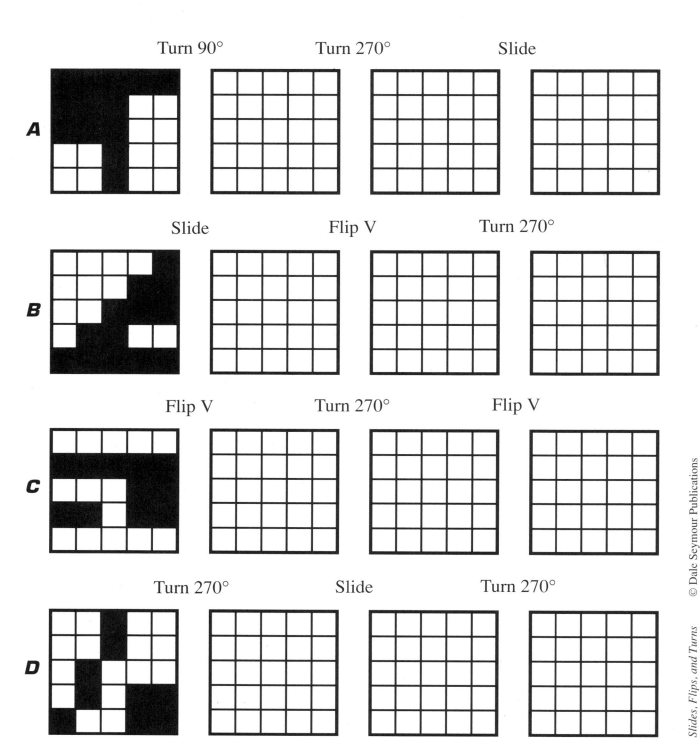

Slides, Flips, and Turns

Shading Combinations 2

Shade the grids to show the results of the slides, flips, and turns across the rows.

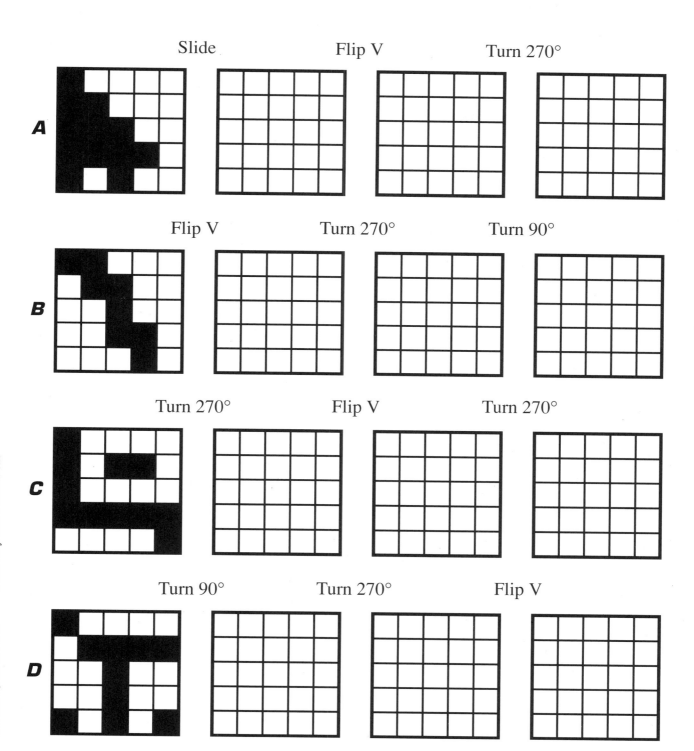

Slides, Flips, and Turns

Shading Combinations 3

Shade the grids to show the results of the slides, flips, and turns across the rows.

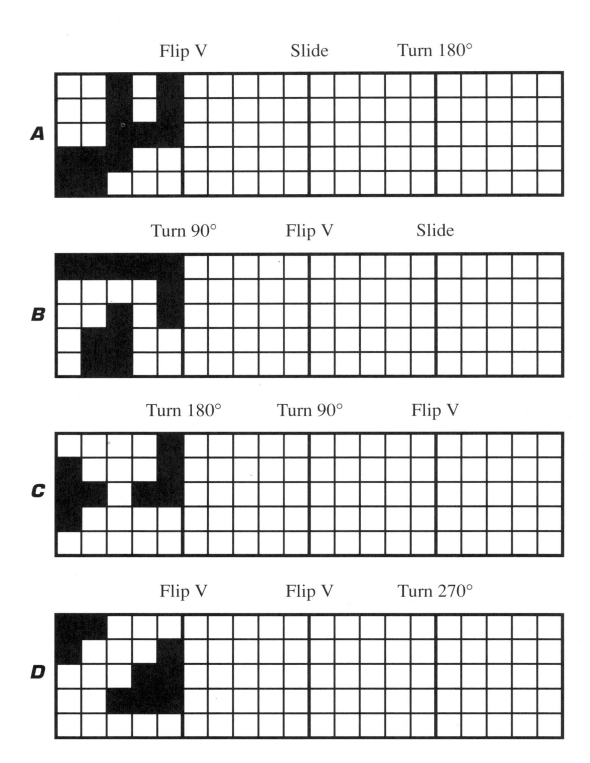

Slides, Flips, and Turns

Shading Combinations 4

Shade the grids to show the results of the slides, flips, and turns down the columns.

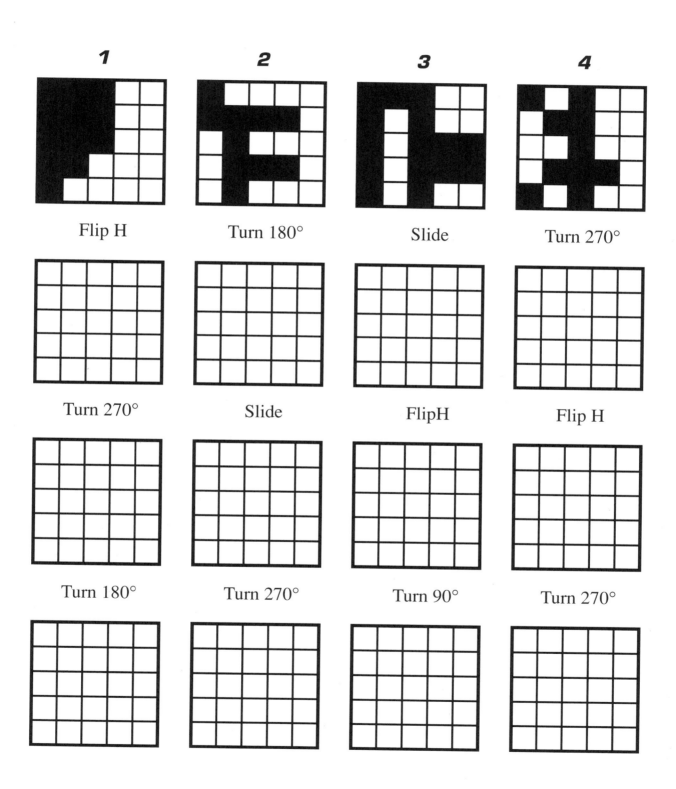

© Dale Seymour Publications

Slides, Flips, and Turns

Shading Combinations 5

Shade the grids to show the slides, flips, and turns across the rows. You will need to work backwards to determine some of the patterns.

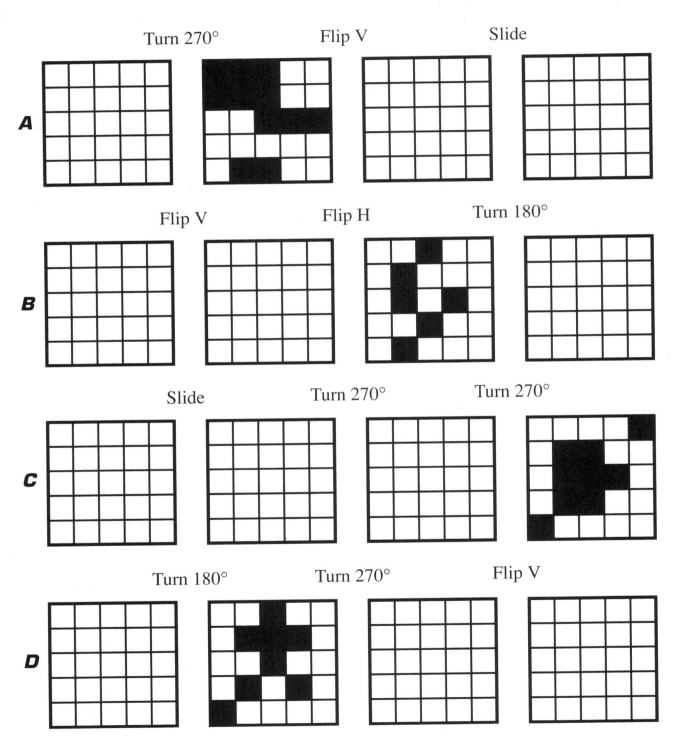

Slides, Flips, and Turns

Shading Combinations 6

Shade the grids to show the slides, flips, and turns across the rows. You will need to work backwards to determine some of the patterns.

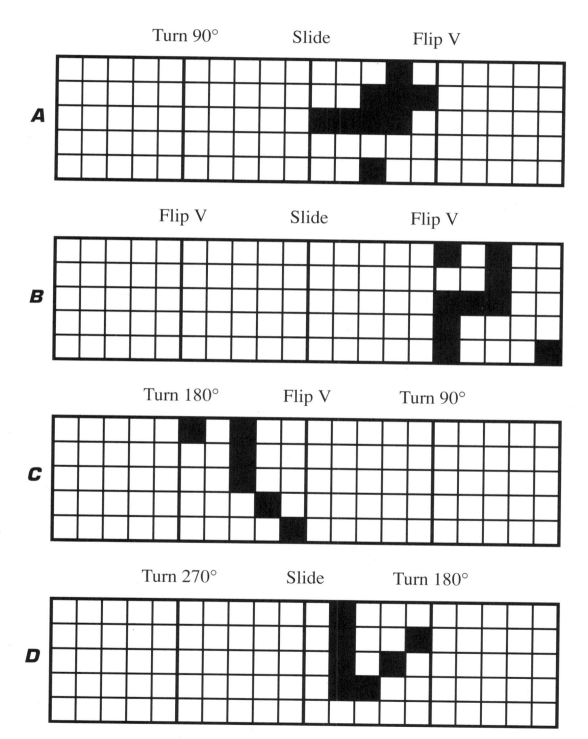

Shading Combinations 7

Shade the grids to show the slides, flips, and turns down the columns. You will need to work backwards to determine some of the patterns.

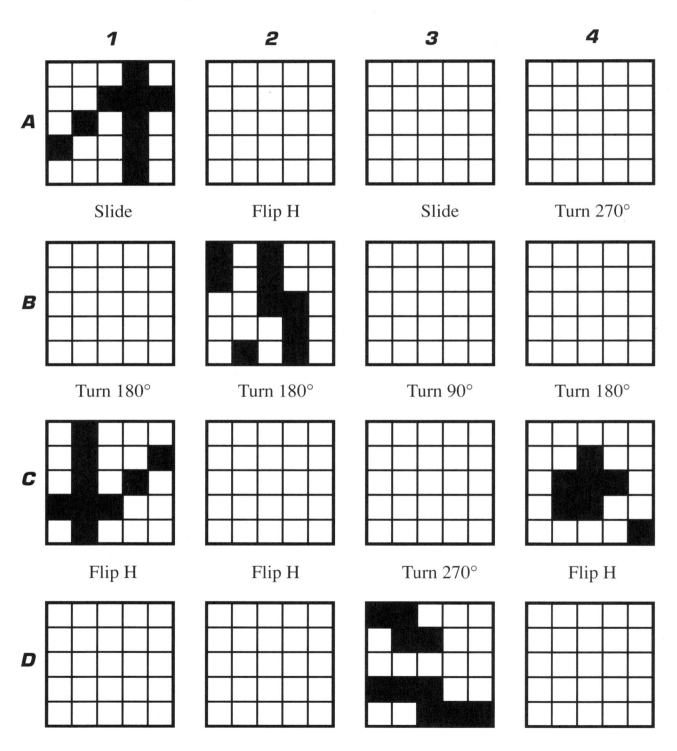

Slides, Flips, and Turns

Shading Combinations 8

Shade the grids to show the indicated motions or analyze the grids and give the motion. You will need to work backwards to determine some of the patterns.

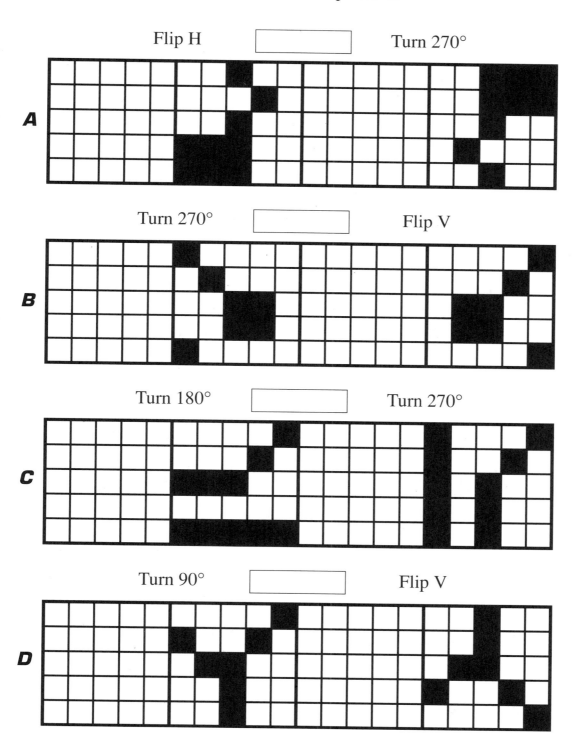

Flip H   Turn 270°

A

Turn 270°   Flip V

B

Turn 180°   Turn 270°

C

Turn 90°   Flip V

D

Shading Combinations 9

Shade the grids to show the indicated motions or analyze the grids and give the motion. You will need to work backwards to determine some of the patterns.

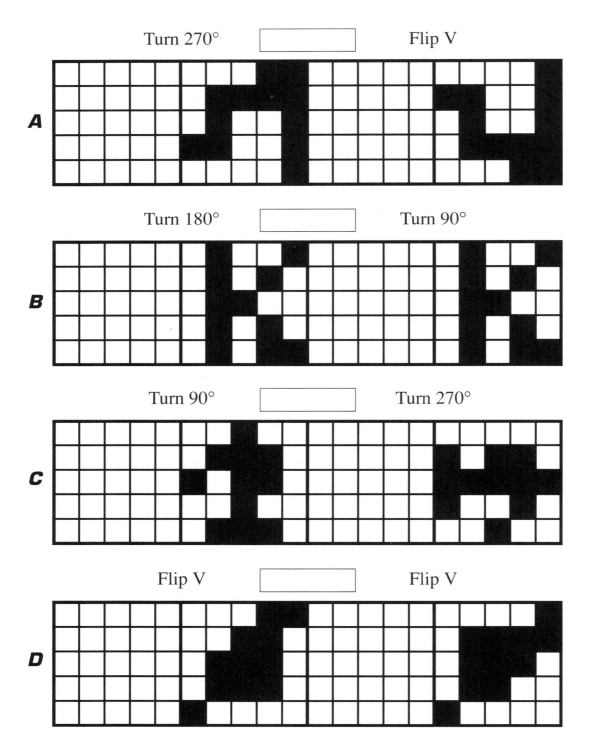

Slides, Flips, and Turns

Shading Combinations 10

Shade the grids to show the indicated motions or analyze the grids and give the motion down each column. You will need to work backwards to determine some of the patterns.

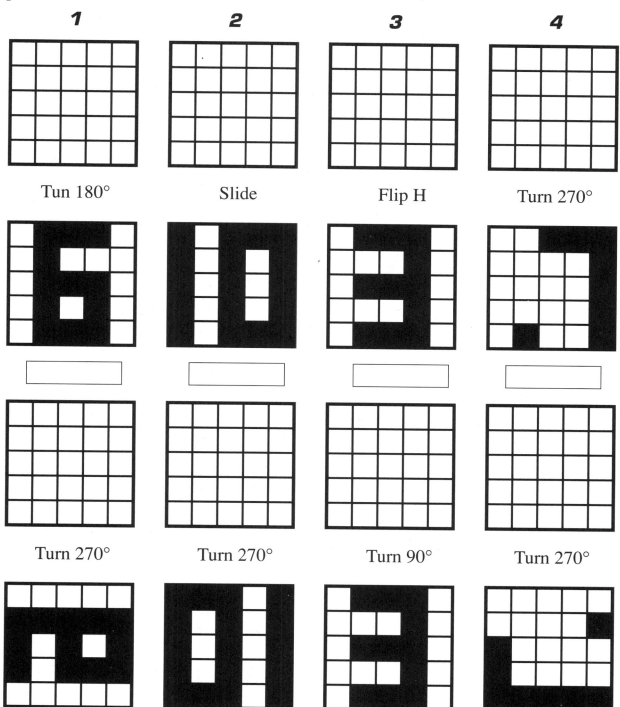

1 Tun 180°

2 Slide

3 Flip H

4 Turn 270°

Turn 270°

Turn 270°

Turn 90°

Turn 270°

Analyzing Combinations 1

Analyze the motion used to change one grid pattern into the next pattern across the rows. Write your result in the box above the grids.

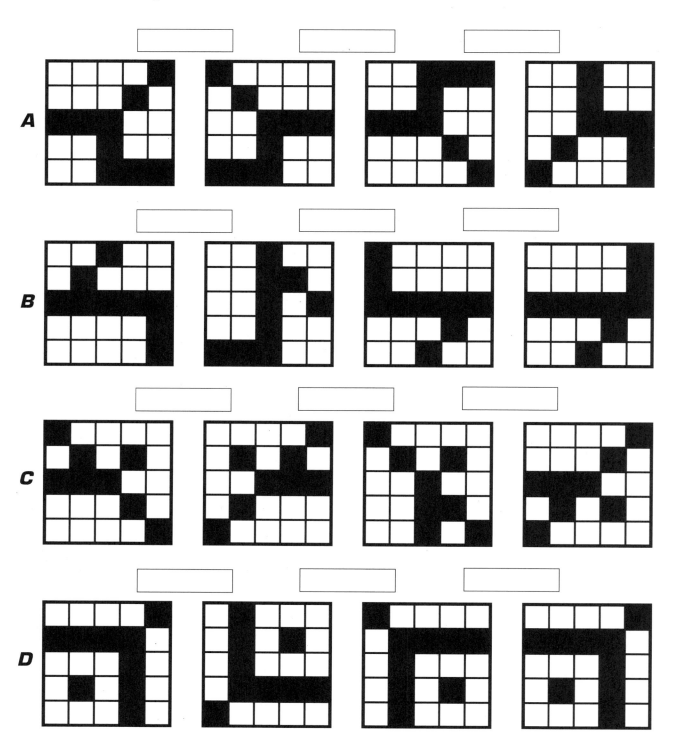

Analyzing Combinations 2

Analyze the motion used to change one grid pattern into the next pattern across the rows. Write your result in the box above the grids.

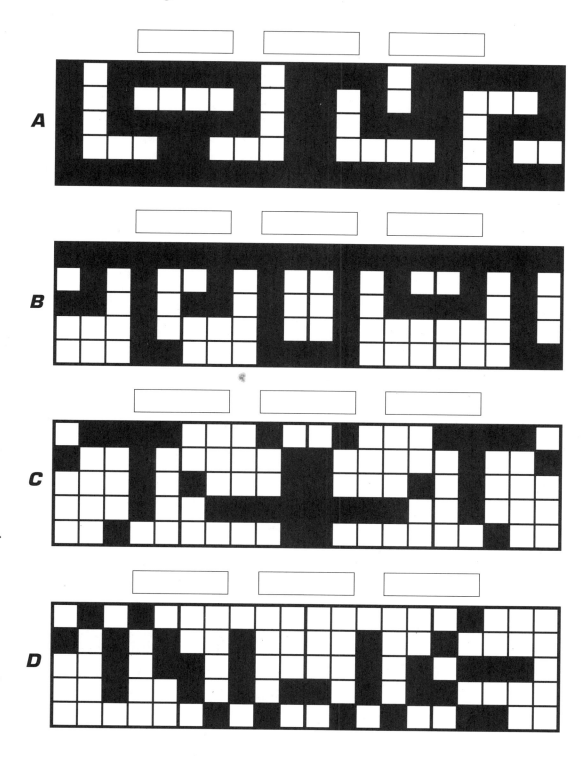

Analyzing Combinations 3

Analyze the motion used to change a grid pattern into the one below it. Write your result in the box between the grids.

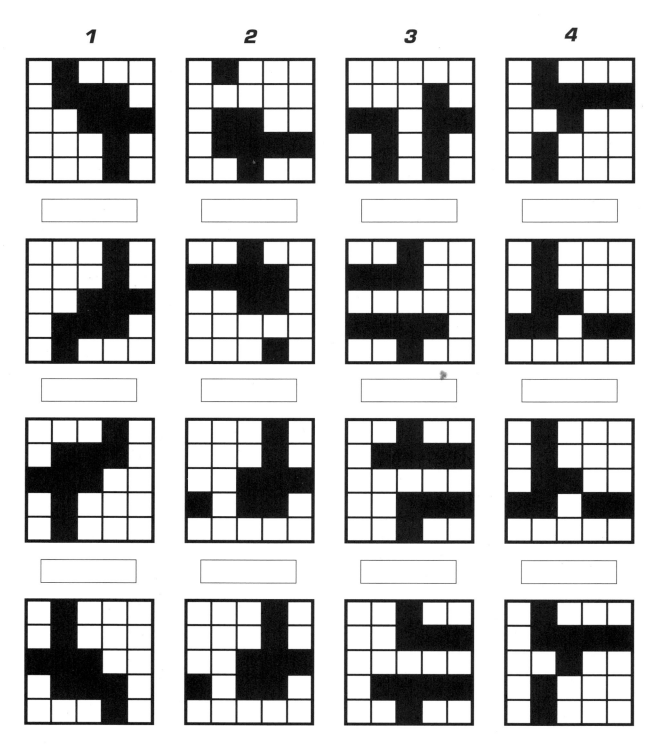

Slides, Flips, and Turns

Analyzing Combinations 4

Analyze the motion used to change a grid pattern into the one below it. Write your result in the box between the grids.

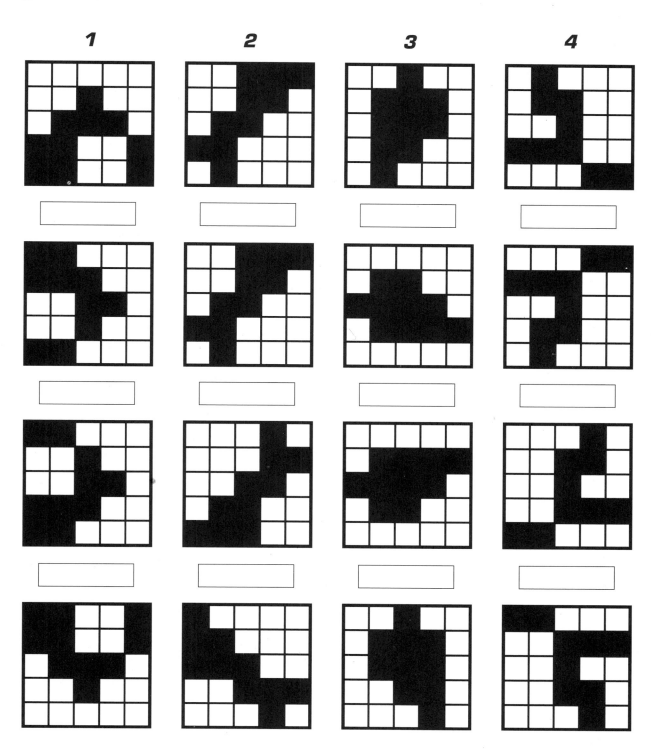

Matching Images 1

Identify the grid that fits the description given.

Start with Grid	Do the Motion	End with Grid
1. A-1	Turn 180°	_____
2. C-2	Flip V	_____
3. C-1	Flip V	_____
4. A-3	Turn 180°	_____
5. B-3	Turn 90°	_____
6. D-1	Turn 180°	_____
7. B-2	Turn 270°	_____
8. C-3	Flip V	_____

Slides, Flips, and Turns

Matching Images 2

Identify the motion that relates the grids.

Start with Grid	Do the Motion	End with Grid
1. C-3	_____	D-2
2. A-2	_____	D-3
3. B-2	_____	D-1
4. B-1	_____	B-3
5. C-3	_____	A-3
6. C-1	_____	A-2
7. A-1	_____	C-2
8. C-3	_____	B-4

Slides, Flips, and Turns

Matching Images 3

Identify the grid that fits the description given.

Start with Grid	Do the Motion	End with Grid
1. C-2	Turn 270°	_____
2. A-1	Turn 90°	_____
3. D-2	Flip H	_____
4. A-3	Turn 90°	_____
5. B-3	Turn 90°	_____
6. B-2	Turn 180°	_____
7. A-2	Flip V	_____
8. B-1	Flip V	_____

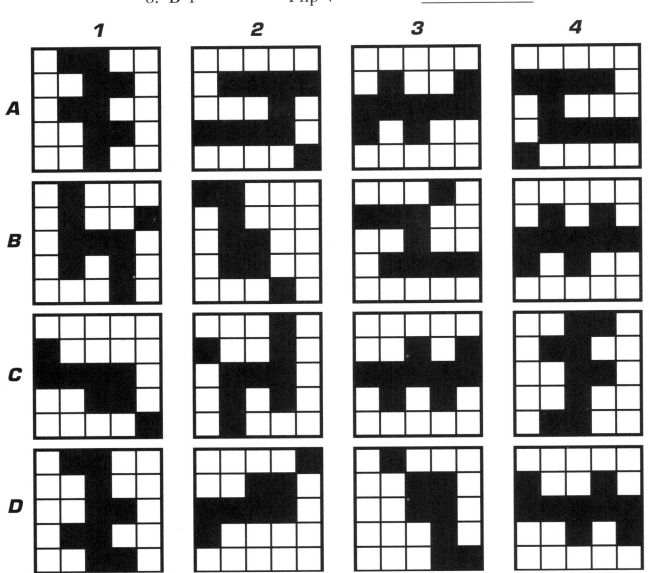

Matching Images 4

Identify the grid that fits the description given.

Start with Grid	First Motion	Second Motion	End with Grid
1. D-2	Turn 180°	Flip V	_____
2. A-1	Flip H	Flip V	_____
3. D-2	Flip H	Turn 90°	_____
4. A-1	Turn 270°	Flip H	_____
5. C-1	Turn 270°	Flip H	_____
6. C-3	Flip V	Turn 90°	_____
7. A-3	Turn 90°	Flip H	_____
8. D-1	Turn 180°	Flip V	_____

1   **2**   **3**   **4**

A

B

C

D

Slides, Flips, and Turns

Matching Negative Images 1

Identify the grid that fits the description. You will be
looking for the negative image of the grid.

Start with Grid	*Do the Motion*	*End with the Negative of Grid*
1. D-2	Turn 90°	_____
2. A-3	Turn 270°	_____
3. C-1	Turn 180°	_____
4. C-4	Turn 270°	_____
5. C-3	Flip V	_____
6. C-2	Flip H	_____
7. D-2	Flip H	_____
8. A-3	Flip V	_____

1   **2**   **3**   **4**

A

B

C

D

Slides, Flips, and Turns

Matching Negative Images 2

Identify the grid that fits the description. You will be looking for the negative image of the grid.

Start with Grid	Do the Motion	End with the Negative of Grid
1. C-2	Flip V	_____
2. B-1	Turn 270°	_____
3. C-3	Turn 90°	_____
4. D-2	Turn 90°	_____
5. C-4	Turn 180°	_____
6. D-3	Turn 180°	_____
7. C-1	Turn 270°	_____
8. D-4	Flip H	_____

Slides, Flips, and Turns

Shading Full-Grid Combinations 1

Using the one shaded grid, follow the directions in the table to complete the shading of the entire pattern. Complete the vertical moves down the first column, then go across the rows.

	1	2	3	4
A		Slide	Flip V	Flip V
B	Flip H	Turn 180°	Slide	Turn 180°
C	Turn 270°	Turn 180°	Turn 270°	Flip V
D	Flip H	Turn 90°	Flip V	Turn 180°

Slides, Flips, and Turns

Shading Full-Grid Combinations 2

Using the one shaded grid, follow the directions in the table to complete the shading of the entire pattern. Complete the vertical moves down the first column, then go across the rows.

	1	2	3	4
A		Turn 90°	Turn 270°	Slide
B	Turn 180°	Flip V	Slide	Turn 270°
C	Turn 270°	Slide	Turn 180°	Turn 270°
D	Flip H	Turn 270°	Flip V	Turn 90°

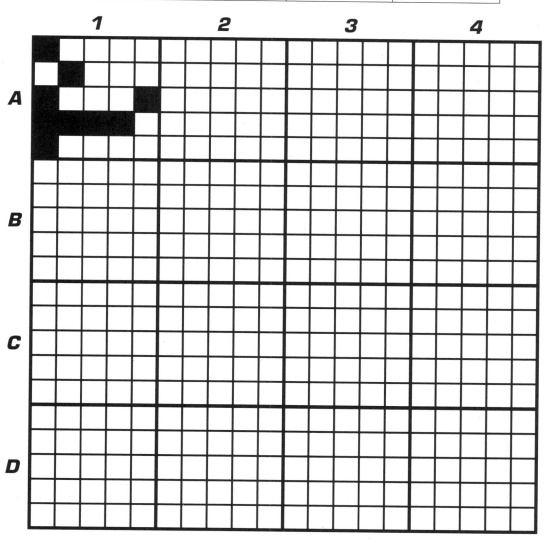

Analyzing Full-Grid Combinations 1

Starting with the grid in the upper left-hand corner, analyze and identify the motion used to change one grid into the next, start by going down the first column, then go across the rows. Write your answers in the table.

	1	2	3	4
A				
B				
C				
D				

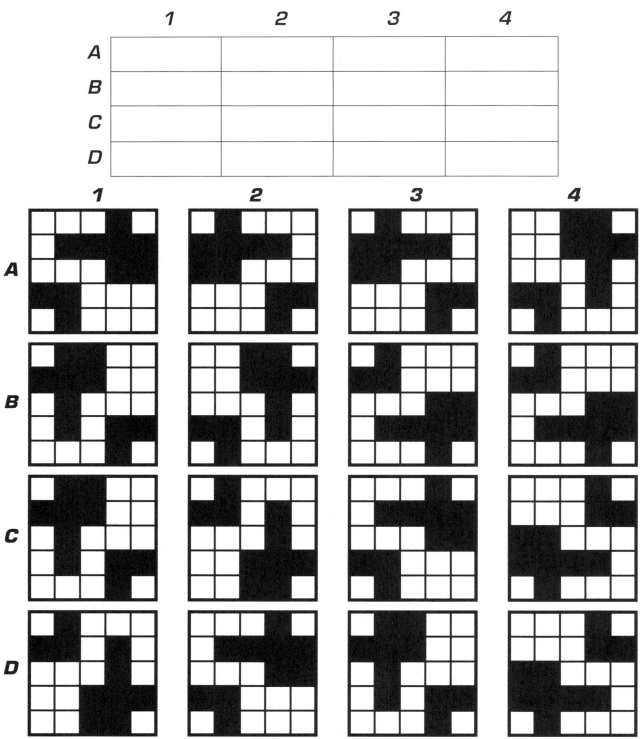

Slides, Flips, and Turns

Analyzing Full-Grid Combinations 2

Starting with the grid in the upper left-hand corner, analyze and identify the motion used to change one grid into the next, start by going down the first column, then go across the rows. Write your answers in the table.

	1	2	3	4
A				
B				
C				
D				

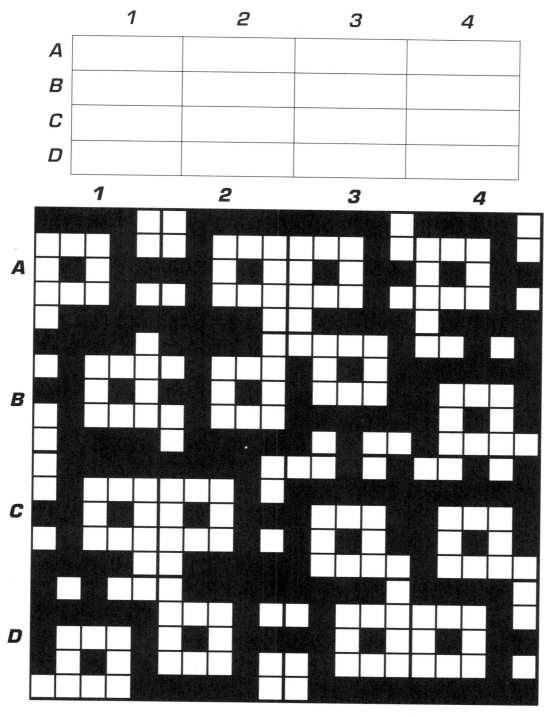

Shading Diagonal Patterns 1

Before shading the slide, flip, or turn indicated, use a straightedge to draw lines corresponding to those in the first grid.

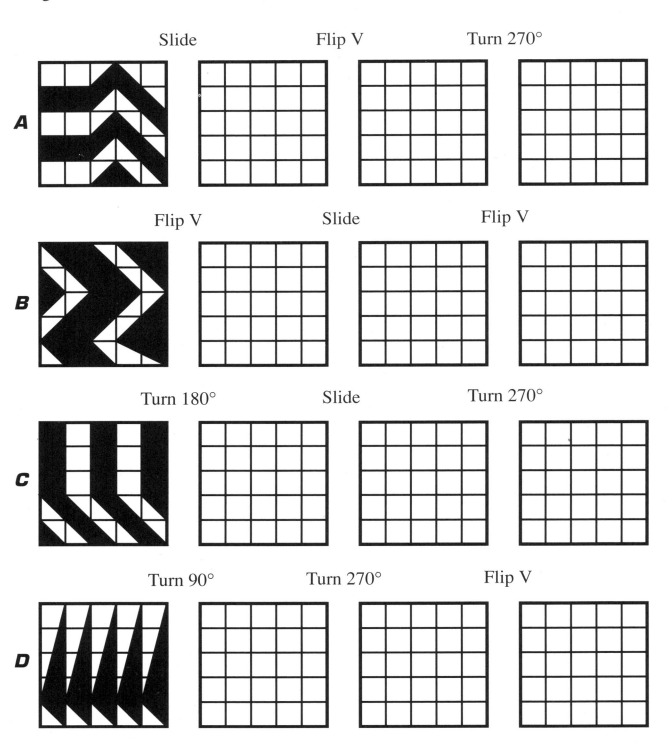

Shading Diagonal Patterns 2

Before shading the slide, flip, or turn indicated, use a
straightedge to draw lines corresponding to those in the
first grid.

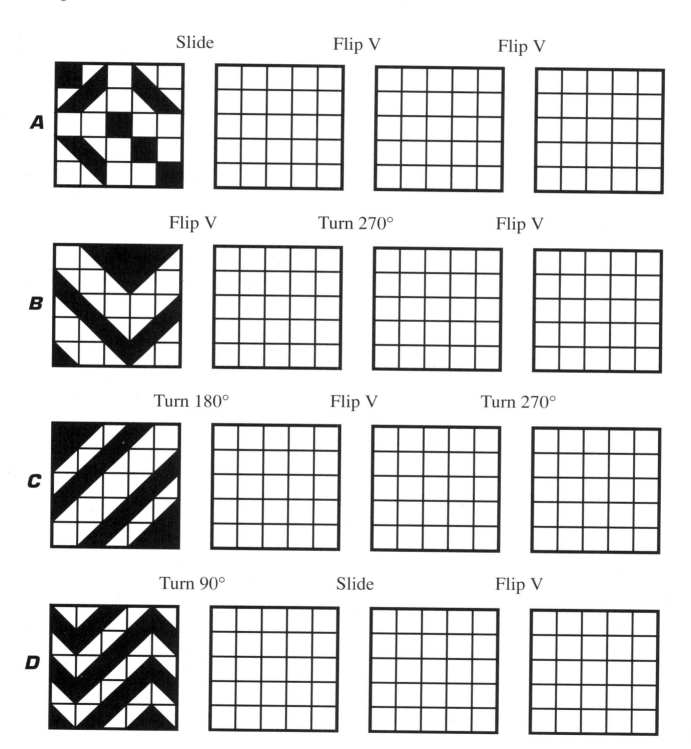

Analyzing Diagonal Patterns 1

Analyze the motion used to change one grid pattern into the next pattern. Write each result in the box above the grids.

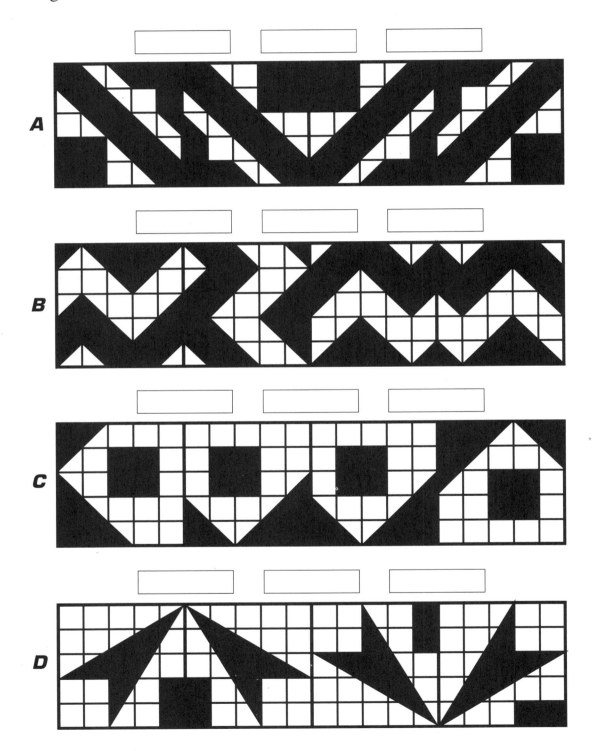

Slides, Flips, and Turns   © Dale Seymour Publications

Part Two
Other Patterns

Shading Single Reflections 3

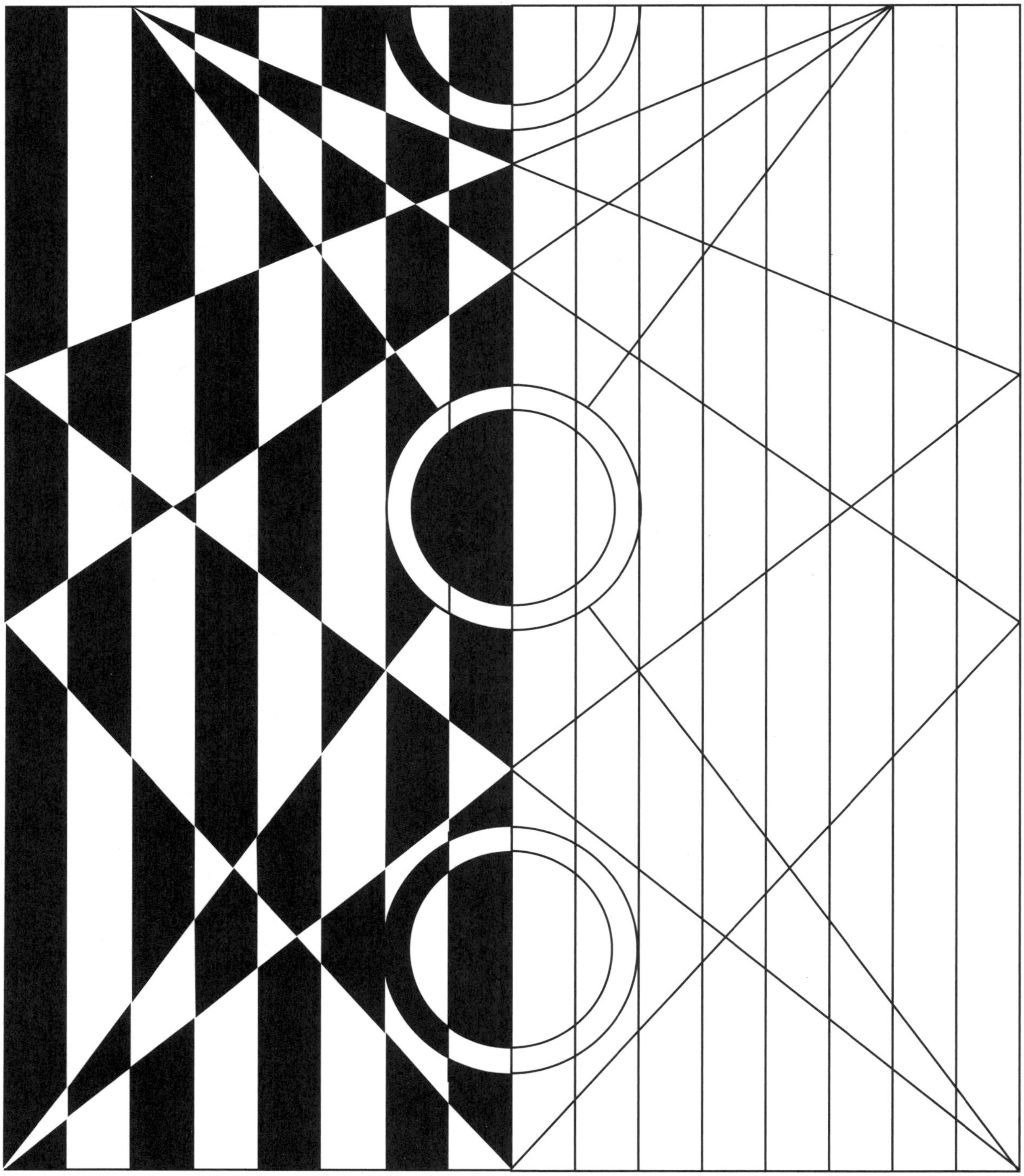

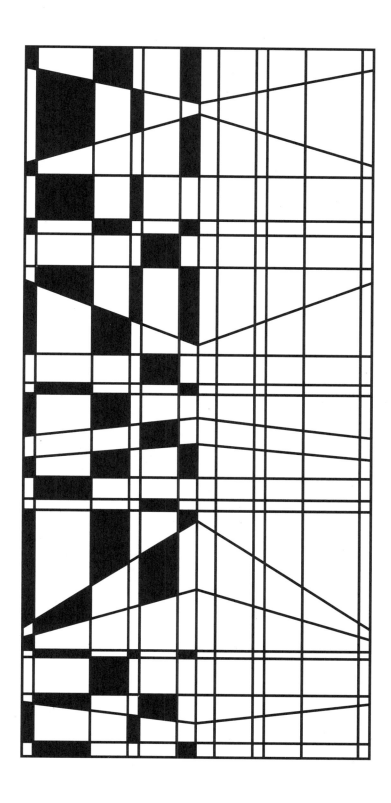

Slides, Flips, and Turns

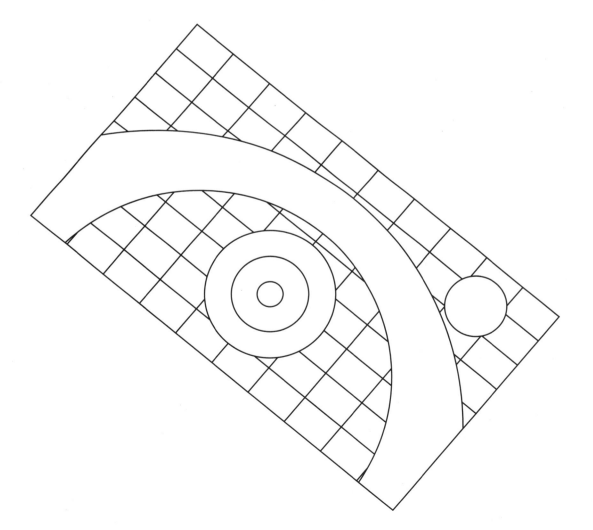

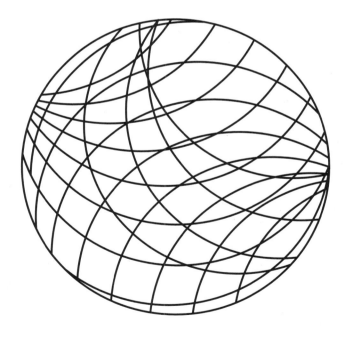

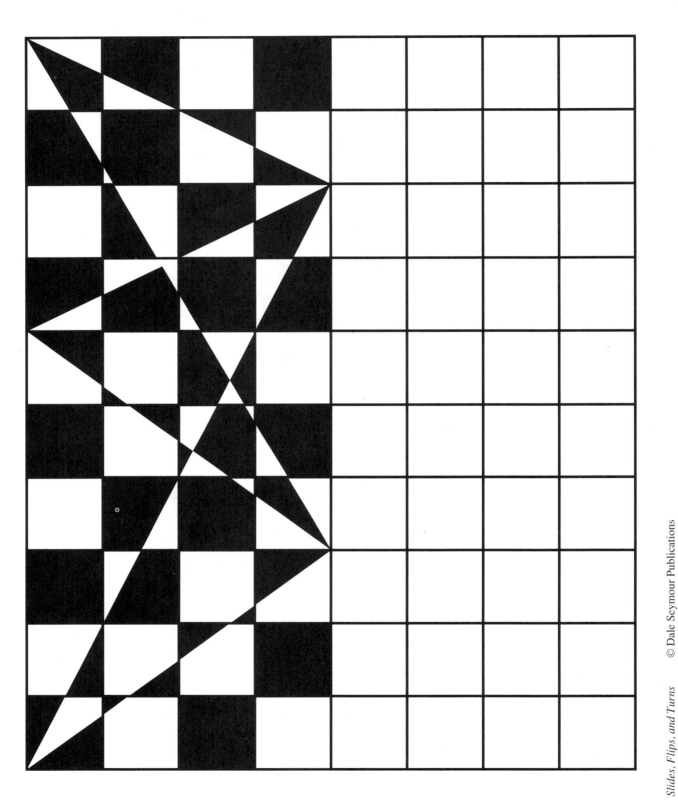

Slides, Flips, and Turns

Answers

Page 20

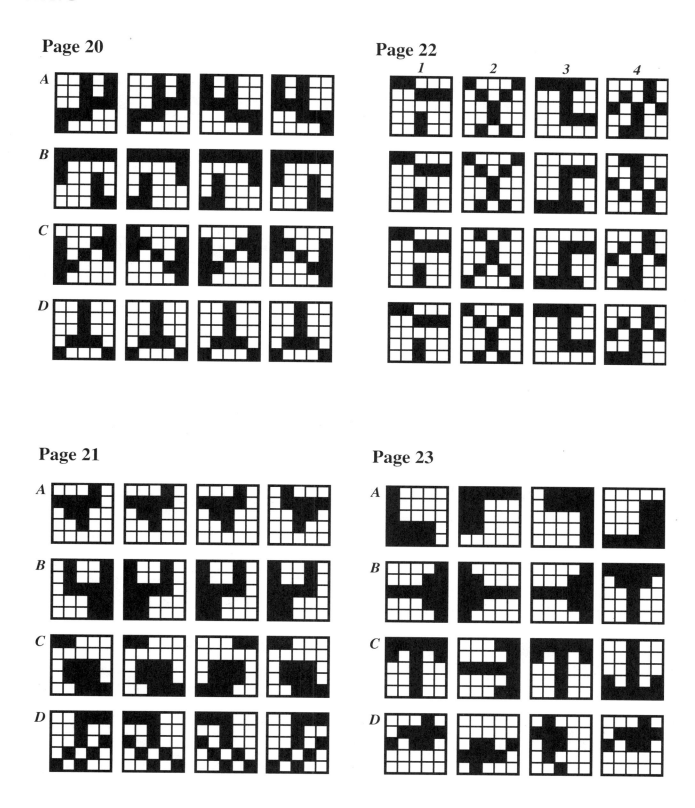

Page 21

Page 22

Page 23

Answers

Page 24

A

B

C

D

Page 25

1   2   3   4

Page 26

A

B

C

D

Page 27

A

B

C

D

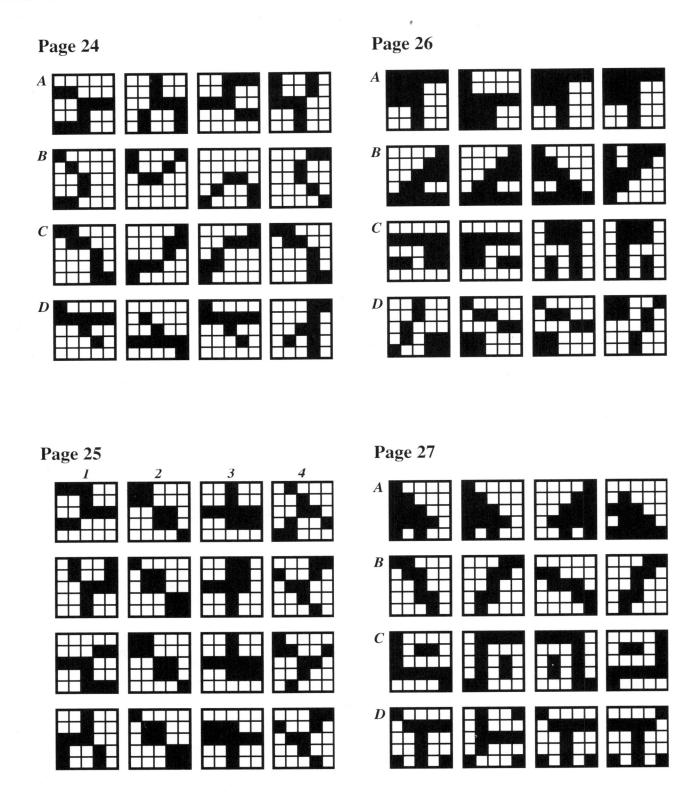

Answers

Page 28

A

B

C

D

Page 30

A

B

C

D

Page 29

1   2   3   4

Page 31

A

B

C

D

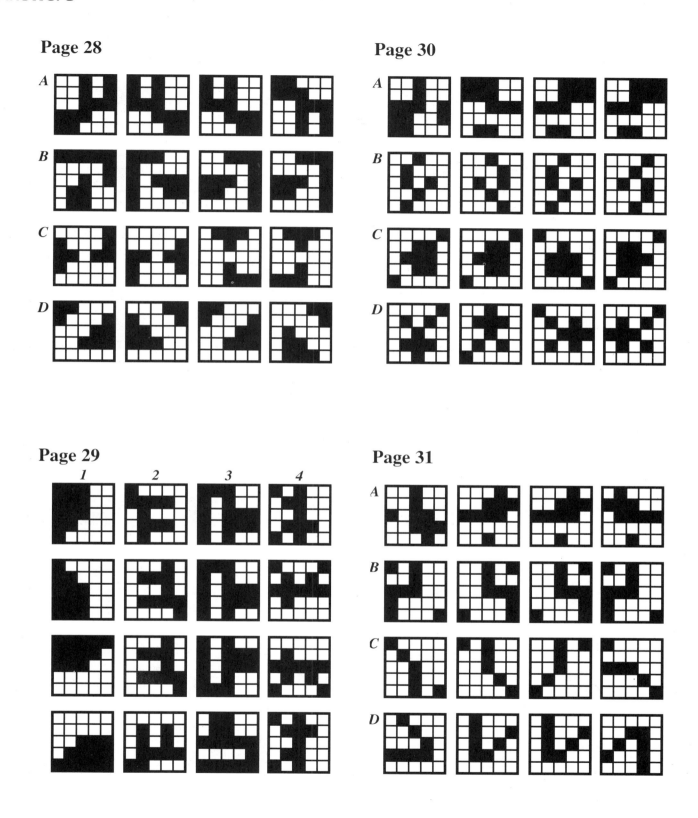

Answers

Page 32

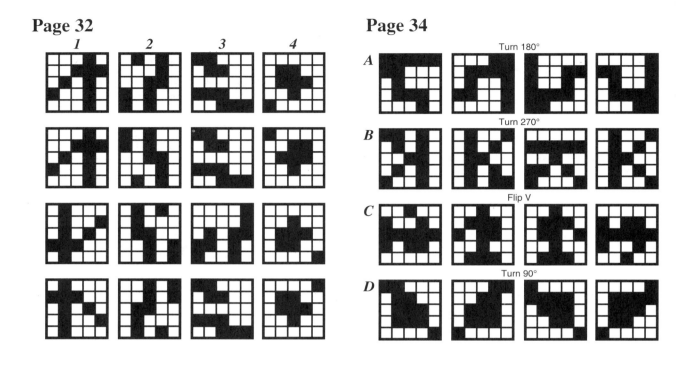

Page 33

Page 34

Page 35

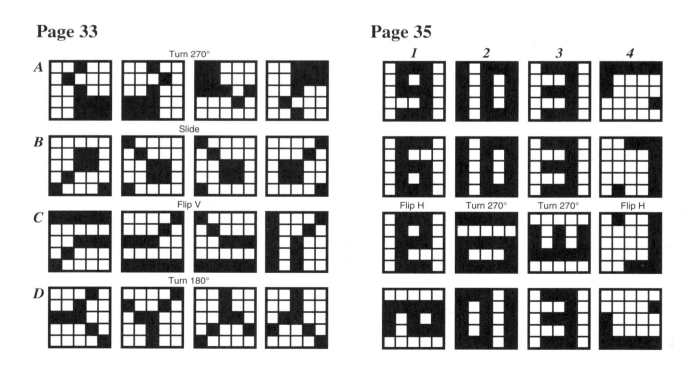

Answers

Page 36
A. Flip V, Turn 180°, Turn 270°
B. Turn 270°, Turn 270°, Flip V
C. Flip V, Turn 270°, Turn 270°
D. Turn 180°, Turn 270°, Flip V

Page 37
A. Flip V, Turn 270°, Turn 270°
B. Slide, Flip V, Flip V
C. Turn 270°, Flip V, Turn 270°
D. Turn 180°, Flip V, Turn 270°

Page 38
1. Flip H, Turn 180°, Flip H
2. Turn 180°, Turn 270°, Slide
3. Turn 270°, Turn 180°, Flip H
4. Turn 90°, Slide, Turn 270°

Page 39
1. Turn 270°, Flip H, Turn 270°
2. Slide, Turn 180°, Turn 270°
3. Turn 90°, Flip H, Turn 270°
4. Flip H, Turn 180°, Flip H

Page 40
1. C-2 2. C-4 3. A-3 4. D-2
5. D-1 6. D-4 7. C-3 8. A-2

Page 41
1. Turn 90° 2. Flip V
3. Turn 270° 4. Turn 180°
5. Turn 270° 6. Turn 270°
7. Turn 180° 8. Flip H

Page 42
1. B-3 2. B-4 3. C-1 4. D-1
5. C-2 6. D-3 7. A-4 8. C-2

Page 43
1. C-1 2. C-3 3. B-3 4. D-1
5. A-2 6. D-1 7. B-1 8. B-2

Page 44
1. A-4 2. D-4 3. A-1 4. B-3
5. B-1 6. A-2 7. D-3 8. B-4

Page 45
1. D-4 2. A-4 3. B-1 4. B-4
5. A-1 6. B-3 7. D-1 8. A-3

Page 46

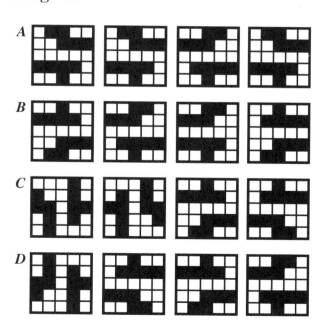

Answers

Page 47

A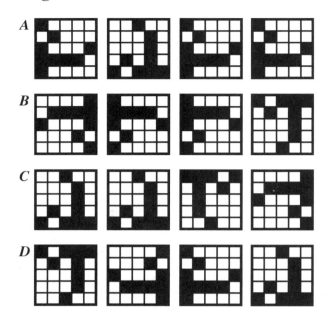

(patterns A, B, C, D shown as grids)

Page 50

A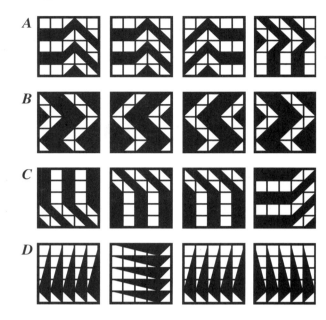

Page 48

	Flip V	Slide	Turn 270°
Turn 90°	Flip V	Turn 270°	Slide
Slide	Turn 180°	Turn 90°	Turn 180°
Turn 180°	Turn 90°	Turn 90°	Turn 90°

Page 49

	Flip V	Flip V	Slide
Turn 180°	Slide	Turn 90°	Turn 180°
Flip H	Flip V	Turn 90°	Slide
Turn 270°	Turn 270°	Flip V	Turn 180°

Page 51

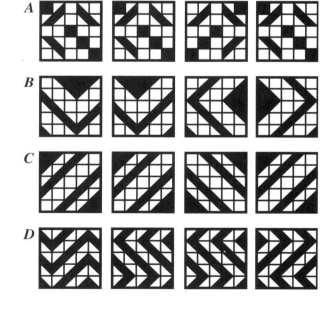

Answers

Page 52
A. Turn 180°, Flip V, Turn 180°
B. Turn 270°, Turn 270°, Flip V
C. Turn 90°, Slide, Turn 180°
D. Flip V, Turn 180°, Turn 270°

The answers for pages 54 to 68 can be checked visually.